science words

Silly Monkey in the Science Lab

by Justin McCory Martin

illustrated by Jim Paillot

SCHOLASTIC INC.

New York • Toronto • London • Auckland • Sydney
Mexico City • New Delhi • Hong Kong • Buenos Aires

No part of this publication may be reproduced, stored in a retrieval system, or transmitted in any form or by any means, electronic, mechanical, photocopying, recording, or otherwise, without written permission of the publisher. For information regarding permission, write to Scholastic Inc., Attention: Permissions Department, 557 Broadway, New York, NY 10012.

Designed by Maria Lilja
ISBN-13: 978-0-545-08855-8 • ISBN-10: 0-545-08855-0
Copyright © 2009 by Scholastic Inc.
All rights reserved. Printed in China.

SCHOLASTIC, VOCABULARY TALES™, and associated logos are trademarks and/or registered trademarks of Scholastic Inc.

First printing, January 2009
12 11 10 9 8 7 6 5 4 3 2 1   9 10 11 12 13 14/0

Building Vocabulary With This Book
This book contains eight key words that are important for all children to know. Read the story straight through for enjoyment. Then read it again, pausing to define and discuss each key word. Follow-up the tale with the fun activities on pages 14–16. When you're done, celebrate—kids will have added eight great words to their vocabularies!

Hi there! My name is Dr. Mavis McGloop. I'm a very serious scientist with a very silly pet monkey. Say hello, Marvin!

Let me show you around my **laboratory**.
This is where I work.

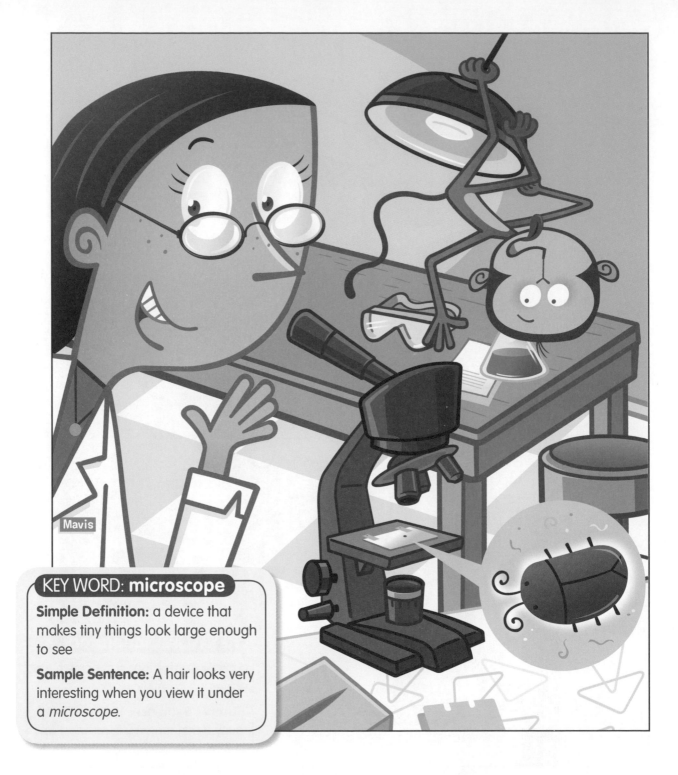

KEY WORD: **microscope**

Simple Definition: a device that makes tiny things look large enough to see

Sample Sentence: A hair looks very interesting when you view it under a *microscope*.

This is my **microscope**. I use it to take a closer look at tiny things. It can make a teeny bug look really huge!

KEY WORD: **magnet**

Simple Definition: a piece of metal that attracts other metal

Sample Sentence: A *magnet* picks up staples, but not paper.

This is my **magnet**. It can pick up metal. Wow, it's even strong enough to pick up this stool!

Let's do an **experiment.** First, I need to put on my special laboratory gloves.

Now, I will put on my **goggles**. Marvin, I know you are back there. Stop being so silly!

Here is a tube filled with a red **solid**. I'll just add a few drops of this blue liquid. What do you think will happen?

KEY WORD: **gas**

Simple Definition: a substance, such as oxygen, that will spread to fill any space that contains it

Sample Sentence: Oxygen is a *gas*, not a liquid or solid.

Cool! It made a purple **gas**!

Let's try another experiment. This one involves my brand-new hat and a very silly monkey.

KEY WORD: prediction

Simple Definition: a guess about what will happen

Sample Sentence: My *prediction* is that we will have a very fun day at the beach today.

To do it, I simply place the hat on my head and make a **prediction**. Here it is: *I predict Marvin is going to LOVE my brand-new hat.*

Yup, just as I predicted. Being a serious scientist is a lot of fun...

when you share your laboratory with a very
silly monkey!

Meaning Match

Listen to the definition. Then go to the WORD CHEST and find a vocabulary word that matches it.

1 a device that makes tiny things look large enough to see

2 a scientific test to see what happens

3 special glasses that fit tightly around your eyes to protect them

4 a substance that is dry and hard

5 a special room for doing scientific work

6 a substance, such as oxygen, that will spread to fill any space that contains it

7 a piece of metal that attracts other metal

8 a guess about what will happen

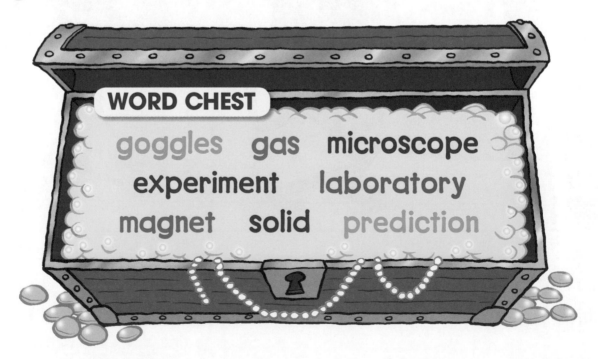

WORD CHEST

goggles   gas   microscope
experiment   laboratory
magnet   solid   prediction

Vocabulary Fill-ins

Listen to the sentence. Then go to the WORD BOX and find the best word to fill in the blank.

WORD BOX

prediction	laboratory	solid	magnet
experiment	microscope	gas	goggles

1. Barry would like to be a scientist and work in a _____ when he grows up.

2. The balloon was filled with a _____ called helium.

3. My grandma bought this cool refrigerator _____ for me.

4. The puddle froze and became _____ ice.

5. The scientist covered her eyes with _____ when she was working.

6. To do this _____, you need a cotton ball, a ruler, and a rubber band.

7. Cindy looked at the dark clouds and made a _____ that it would rain.

8. When Sam looked through the _____, he saw that each teeny piece of salt was shaped like a cube.

Answers: 1. laboratory 2. gas 3. magnet 4. solid 5. goggles 6. experiment 7. prediction 8. microscope

Listen to each question. Think about it. Then answer.

1 Describe how the inside of a **laboratory** would look. Name some of the things you might find there.

2 **Goggles** are worn in laboratories. Why do you think they are important to use?

3 Think of an **experiment** you would like to try. What would it be? What might you learn?

4 What are some things that would stick to a **magnet**? What are some things that would NOT stick to a **magnet**?

5 Can you name three things that are **solids**? Can you name three things that are liquids?

6 Oxygen is a **gas**. Can you think of some words to describe it?

7 What would you like to see under a **microscope**? How do you think it would look?

8 Have you ever made a **prediction** that was right? Have you ever made a **prediction** that was wrong? Tell about them.

Extra: Can you think of some more science words? Make a list.